The
Better
Allies®
Way

A WORKBOOK FOR BEING MORE INCLUSIVE AT WORK

Karen Catlin

Better Allies Press

ALSO BY KAREN CATLIN

Better Allies
Everyday Actions to Create Inclusive, Engaging Workplaces

Belonging in Healthcare
The Better Allies Approach to Creating More Inclusive Workplaces*

The Better Allies Approach to Hiring*

Present! A Techie's Guide to Public Speaking
(with Poornima Vijayashanker)

FIRST EDITION, January 2024

Paperback ISBN: 978-1-7327233-7-5

Editing: Anne Janzer
Cover and interior design: Lucy Giller
Illustration in Welcome chapter: Danielle Coke

Illustrations for each ally type adapted from the "Noun Project" by Adrien Coquet, Dinosoft Labs, unlimicon, Thomas' designs, ProSymbols, Ben Davis, and Iconathon. Licensed under Creative Commons CC BY 3.0.

Author's website: www.karencatlin.com

Contents

Welcome!

I'm Karen Catlin, the author of three books and a popular weekly newsletter about how people can be better allies and create more inclusive workplaces.

A theme woven throughout my writing is that you don't have to be a leader or have the words "Diversity," "Inclusion," or "Belonging" on your business card to make a difference. There are everyday actions we all can take to create more inclusive workplaces. There are myriad ways we can be allies.

Changing entire systems can feel daunting, but wielding privilege as an ally doesn't have to be complicated. We can start with a single act and build from there.

This workbook will lead you through exercises to identify practical steps you can take to make aspects of your workplace culture more inclusive, or to speak up when you see bias crop up in a conversation.

I've organized the exercises using a framework of seven archetypes or roles that allies can play. I initially developed this framework when writing my book, *Better Allies*®, to explore the many ways allies can make a difference. It's been a popular and powerful tool for my readers to understand that there is no single definition of what it means to support colleagues from under-represented groups.

In this workbook, you'll learn about these seven archetypes and answer prompts to help you identify actions to take in each of these roles to level up your impact as an ally.

As you read about each archetype, you may find some that suit you well. Perhaps you're already acting as these kinds of allies naturally. Or, you may feel they're all somewhat foreign. Regardless, my goal is for you to learn new approaches to level up your ally skills under all seven roles.

How to use this workbook

We all know the saying "a journey of a thousand miles begins with a single step" (or push of a wheelchair). Allyship is the same. Whether you're just beginning the allyship journey or have already started, consider this workbook your travel companion.

You may prefer to be a solo traveler, exploring the archetypes and doing the exercises on your own. And that's great!

I've also included activities and discussion prompts for teams who want to level up their ally skills as a group. You'll find them sprinkled throughout this workbook. Consider meeting over 7 weeks, exploring and discussing one ally archetype each time.

Whether you're on your own or learning with others, consider finding an accountability partner. Someone who will help you stay committed to taking the actions you'll identify in the exercises. (More on this on page 83 under "My 30-day plan.")

CURIOUS TO LEARN MORE?

While I designed the workbook to stand on its own, you can learn more about the power of these archetypes and many other examples of everyday actions to be more inclusive in my book, *Better Allies*®. Or, if you work in healthcare, check out the companion book, *Belonging in Healthcare,* filled with stories of how these archetypes show up in inclusive healthcare workplaces.

Now it's time to get started. Up first? Learning about the role of the Sponsor.

After that, you'll learn about the Champion, the Amplifier, the Advocate, the Scholar, the Confidant, and the Upstander.

WHAT'S NOT OKAY

This workbook contains copyrighted material. You can't reproduce it or create videos, discussion cards, or other learning material leveraging its contents.

If you're a meeting facilitator or professional workshop instructor who wants to leverage this workbook, let's talk! Please get in touch with me at info@betterallies.com.

The Sponsor

I once worked for a software company that was acquired by a larger company. In the first few months following the acquisition, I noticed something interesting. My new manager said things in meetings along the lines of "What I learned from Karen Catlin is the following ..."

By doing this, he helped me build credibility with my new colleagues, most of whom were men I'd have to collaborate with on cross-team initiatives. He took action as an ally, using his position of privilege to endorse me publicly. His shout-outs made a difference and definitely made me feel great.

The Sponsor also speaks about someone when they aren't even in the room.

In her TEDWomen talk, which has been viewed over 4 million times, Carla Harris delivered an important message about meritocracy—or lack thereof. She debunked the myth that to get ahead, you just need to do great work and it will be recognized and rewarded. Instead, she points out that you need a sponsor who will brag on your behalf. Someone who is invited to decision-making meetings and is willing to spend some of their hard-earned social capital advocating on your behalf. Someone who has your back.

When recommending someone, the Sponsor endorses them wholeheartedly and enthusiastically, in formal letters, verbal reference checks, backchannel casual conversations, and social media endorsements. Each one can impact the career trajectories of the people they describe. The Sponsor shows complete confidence. No hedging ("she might be good"), faint praise ("she'll do okay"), or other phrases that undermine ("she needs only minimal guidance").

Wondering why I'm calling this out? In a study of recommendations for academic positions, researchers found that letters about women included more doubt-raising phrases than those about men, and that even one such phrase can make a difference in a job search.[1,2] This means that a lukewarm recommendation may be more harmful than no recommendation at all.

An important note: A Sponsor doesn't need to hold a senior leadership role to be an effective ally. People at all levels can act as Sponsors by vocally supporting their coworkers from underrepresented groups in all contexts, specifically in situations that will help boost their standing and reputation.

Now let's dive into some exercises to identify how you can act as a Sponsor.

EXERCISE 1:
GET TO KNOW AND RECOMMEND TALENT FROM UNDERREPRESENTED GROUPS

Sponsors use their social capital to recommend people for opportunities, often by singing their praises when they're not around.

Think about who you sponsor. If they tend to be the same gender, race, sexual orientation/identity, or age as you, or if they remind you of your younger self, consider developing relationships with a more diverse group of coworkers — and start opening some doors for them.

Write the names of a few people you've recently recommended for an opportunity and what it was.

NAME	I RECOMMENDED THEM FOR

Circle or highlight those who are the same gender, race, or other identity as you. What does this tell you?

....

....

....

....

....

....

....

....

....

....

....

....

....

....

....

Now think of some other colleagues who are members of underrepresented groups. Do you know them well enough to recommend them for similar opportunities in the future? If not, list some ways you can learn more about their work and skill sets.

COWORKER'S NAME	I WILL RECOMMEND THEM FOR THIS KIND OF OPPORTUNITY, OR GET TO KNOW THEM BETTER BY

EXERCISE 2:
ENDORSE COWORKERS

Sharing what you learned from someone, as my manager did in the story above, is just one approach to vocally supporting coworkers from under-represented groups to boost their standing and reputation.

As allies, we can also endorse people by reacting positively to points they raise in meetings, shared documents, and online discussion forums. And, if our company has a peer-nominated spot bonus program, we can submit a coworker's name along with a brief description of a recent accomplishment. We can also write powerful letters of recommendation.

Reflect on how you tend to endorse coworkers. Write a few examples here.

....

....

....

....

....

....

....

....

....

....

Identify one or more actions you'll take to do even more of it, especially for coworkers from underrepresented groups.

IDEA	MY NEXT STEP
SHARE SOMETHING I LEARNED FROM THEM WITH OTHERS	
IN VIRTUAL MEETINGS AND SHARED DOCUMENTS, USE POSITIVE EMOJI REACTIONS OR ADD SUPPORTIVE COMMENTS (E.G., "FANTASTIC IDEA" OR "100% WHAT JO SAID")	
NOMINATE THEM FOR AWARDS OR PEER BONUSES	
OFFER TO GIVE A RECOMMEN- DATION OR WRITE A LINKEDIN ENDORSEMENT FOR A RECENT PROJECT THEY WORKED ON	

EXERCISE 3:
SUPPORT GROUPS THAT SERVE UNDERREPRESENTED EMPLOYEES

As Sponsors, we can engage with Employee Resource Groups (ERGs) or Affinity Groups that serve underrepresented employees by providing support and career development opportunities. We can attend their events to demonstrate our support and learn more about their members and their experiences.

To expand our understanding, we can join an industry-wide webinar or conference focused on an underrepresented demographic. Search online to find ones for your area of interest. For example, "women in medicine event" or "Latinas in tech conference."

Another way to support these groups is financially. If we oversee a budget, we might be able to underwrite some or all of an event. Or we could appeal to someone with budget authority to consider sponsoring them.

Identify an ERG at your organization or an industry-wide group for an underrepresented demographic you'd like to learn more about. Write it here.

....

....

....

....

....

....

Reach out to the group's leaders to see if you can attend an upcoming event to listen and learn as an ally. Ask if they need support for their event, such as getting the word out, staffing a check-in table, cleaning up afterward, or sponsoring it financially. Note the name of the event, the date, and how you'll support it here.

EVENT NAME	
DATE	
I'LL SUPPORT IT BY	

When you attend the event, pay attention to ideas that your organization could act on to be more inclusive. Ask how you can help advocate for these ideas. Here's space to write a few notes about it.

....

....

....

....

....

....

....

....

....

....

....

....

....

....

....

....

....

....

....

Last but not least, if you're a senior leader, offer to be the executive sponsor for an ERG. Reach out to your company's ERG coordinator (if you have one), Chief Diversity Officer, or someone you know in human resources and tell them you'd like to be considered if an ERG is looking for a sponsor.

Write the name of the person you'll contact and when you'll contact them (e.g., "before I move on to the next exercise," or "by the end of the week"):

....

....

....

TEAM EXERCISE:
DISCUSS HOW TO BE A SPONSOR IN YOUR WORKPLACE

If you're doing this workbook with others, perhaps you have a role model among you. Who is the likeliest Sponsor, and why?

....

....

....

....

....

....

....

....

....

....

....

....

....

....

Ask the group if others want to step into this role, and if they need any help to be an effective Sponsor. Below, write ideas for ways you can assist them. Or, if you're interested in doing more sponsorship, write your next steps here:

....

....

....

....

....

....

....

....

....

....

....

....

....

....

....

....

....

....

Now step back and reflect on your larger organization. Identify people who are effective Sponsors for employees from underrepresented groups. What actions do they take that stand out (and that you could imagine doing yourself)?

NAME OF SPONSOR	WHAT MAKES THEM EFFECTIVE?

The Champion

A few years ago, Andrew Grill was a global managing partner at IBM and a speaker at the Online Influence Conference. He was on a panel along with five other men when a woman in the audience posed the obvious question to the all-male lineup: "Where are the women?"

The moderator then asked the panelists to address the topic of gender diversity, and Grill, after sharing some of his thoughts, quickly realized he wasn't the best person to respond. In fact, none of the panelists were. He instead asked the woman who raised the question, Miranda Bishop, to take his place onstage. By stepping aside, Grill made a bold statement in support of gender diversity and championed Bishop at the same time.[3]

More recently, when Dr. Githinji Gitahi, CEO of Amref Health Africa, found himself on an all-male panel of experts discussing health and climate change at the 76th World Health Assembly, he staged a walkout. Gitahi headed off the stage and into the audience, saying, "I feel very uncomfortable being on this male panel." He added, "I would like to ask any woman who has insights on this topic to replace me."[4]

The organizer then invited a woman from the audience to join them, and another male panelist swapped his place with a woman colleague. With some gender diversity onstage, Gitahi then rejoined the panel.

All-male panels (known as "manels") are so widespread in many fields that an increasing number of individuals and organizations are pledging to eradicate them. For example, *The Lancet,* a medical journal, adopted a No All-Male Panel Policy in 2019, acknowledging that the traditional predominance of male speakers excludes the full breadth of available expertise and opinion. Their editors will not serve as panelists at public conferences or events when there are no women on the panels, and they're committed to gender balance in events they sponsor or organize.

Some public speakers have added "Won't speak on all-male panels" to their online bios. White people of any gender can use a version that says, "Won't speak on all-white panels." (I've done this myself.)

I've also seen leaders turn a speaking opportunity into a showcase of underrepresented talent. Instead of delivering a keynote at the Grace Hopper Conference herself, Megan Smith (then CTO for the United States) asked six women colleagues from the U.S. Digital Service to join her as panelists to share the work they were doing.[5]

Grill, Gitahi, Smith, and editors at *The Lancet* are shining examples of Champions. When an ally takes on this role, they act similarly to the Sponsor but do so in more public, external venues. They work in solidarity with initiatives designed to promote more inclusion, taking public stances.

Champions also willingly defer to colleagues from underrepresented groups in industry-wide events and conferences, sending meaningful messages to large audiences.

Here are some specific ways to act as a Champion, even if you aren't a frequent public speaker like the people highlighted above:

- Direct questions about specific topics to those with subject-matter expertise instead of answering them yourself.

- Advocate for more women, people of color, and members of other underrepresented groups as speakers and panelists at events.
- If you are asked to take a leadership role on a professional committee or speak on a panel, and you know someone from an underrepresented group who'd be an equally good fit (or better), recommend that person (after asking them first if they'd like you to put them forward).
- Be vocal and genuine in supporting policies and initiatives to create more inclusive workplaces.

How will you show up as a Champion? Here are some exercises to help you identify actions you can take.

EXERCISE 1:
SHARE THE SPOTLIGHT

Many of us have moments of being highly visible. Other teams in our company might consult us for our subject matter expertise. We might be tapped to give presentations or project updates. We might have large followings on social media or a lot of credibility in a corporate online discussion forum. Or, we have large professional networks that result in invitations to loads of fun activities.

Each time we're in the proverbial spotlight, we have an opportunity to shine it on someone else, especially someone who is underestimated, overlooked, and underrepresented.

Reflect on situations when you feel highly visible. Jot down a few.

What will you do to share your spotlight with a member of an under-represented group?

....

....

....

....

....

....

....

....

....

....

....

....

....

....

....

....

....

....

....

EXERCISE 2:
REDIRECT MISDIRECTED QUESTIONS

A "misdirected question" is when someone addresses their question to someone who looks like they have authority instead of asking the most qualified person, who happens to be a woman or a member of another underrepresented group. And it's not just men who are guilty of this phenomenon because people of all gender identities are taught to assume that men naturally hold more power.

As Champions, we can redirect questions to the most qualified person. All it takes is a simple "Deepa is the expert on that topic. Let's hear from her." Or "Including our founder, Elizabeth, on this email. She's the best person to answer your question."

Think about the various places employees, clients, patients, customers, and members of professional associations ask questions. E.g., email, Slack, hallways, meetings, conferences, and social media. Write a few of them here:

....

....

....

....

....

....

....

Have you witnessed any misdirected questions recently? If so, did you or someone else redirect the question? Write a few notes about what happened here:

....
....
....
....
....
....
....
....
....
....
....
....
....
....
....
....
....
....
....

How will you respond the next time this happens?

....

....

....

....

....

....

....

....

....

....

....

....

....

....

....

....

....

....

EXERCISE 3:
BROADCAST YOUR SUPPORT FOR INCLUSION

In addition to the above example of adding "won't speak on all-male or all-white panels" to an online bio, there are many ways to be loud and proud about our support for more inclusive workplaces. Here are some ideas (check those that you already are doing):

☐ Add my pronouns to an email signature, name tag lanyard, video conference account, or online profile such as LinkedIn. Doing so can help normalize this practice and make it easier for coworkers to share theirs.

☐ Join a diversity-related channel in our organization's online discussion forum such as Slack or Teams, and contribute to the conversations.

☐ Change my video conference background to a diversity-themed one. (Many organizations create branded ones for Pride, Women's History Month, Juneteenth, and other diversity-related celebrations throughout the year.)

☐ Write "Aspiring ally" on a conference badge to let others know this is a skill I'm developing.

☐ Celebrate a local Pride parade with coworkers.

What other ways do you broadcast your support for diversity and inclusion?

....

....

....

....

....

....

....

....

....

....

....

....

....

....

....

....

....

....

What's one additional action you'll commit to doing?

....
....
....
....
....
....
....
....
....
....
....
....
....
....
....
....
....
....

TEAM EXERCISE:
DISCUSS HOW TO BE A CHAMPION IN YOUR WORKPLACE

If you're doing this workbook as a team, tap into your collective knowledge of how to be an effective Champion within your organization and any related professional communities.

Who are the Champions? How do they publicly support underrepresented individuals or groups?

NAME OF CHAMPION	WHAT ACTIONS DO THEY TAKE TO PUBLICLY SUPPORT OTHERS?

Circle the actions you'd like to do more of yourself.

The Amplifier

Let's say a person of color says something insightful or even game-changing in a meeting, only to have it dismissed or ignored. Then someone else says the same thing later, and it's well-received — or maybe even heralded. While the second person gets the kudos, whoever originally shared the idea may start fuming inside.

This scenario is all too common, and the frustration is understandable.

Allies can borrow a page from a group of women who figured out how to stop men from stealing their ideas.

In staff meetings during Barack Obama's first term as president, women adopted a strategy they called "amplification." When one of the women staffers made a key point, other women would repeat it and give credit to its author. This approach forced others in the room to recognize the contribution — and denied them the ability to claim it as their own.[6]

Here's one more example. During a webinar hosted by the American Association of Women in Radiology, Dr. Beth McFarland shared a fantastic example of amplifier allyship. She explained how Dr. Susan Asher, a woman more senior than she, would amplify her in meetings. She'd say, "I'd like to reinforce what Beth just said." Those words made McFarland feel what she just said was important, and they helped amplify her point.[7]

Of course, women aren't the only ones who can amplify the voices of other women or members of another underrepresented group. Anyone can do it for someone who is less likely to be heard. I try to do it myself in meetings I attend. Sure, there are times when I'm not quite on the ball, and I miss the opportunity to amplify an idea contributed by someone from an under-represented group. If someone else repeats it later in the meeting, I remind everyone who originated it, saying something like, "Great idea. Thanks to Jing for surfacing it earlier."

And that's not all. I strive to give people credit for saying the same brilliant idea, even if they did so in a previous meeting. Here's what that might look like: "I like that idea a lot. In fact, when Ana brought that up last week, I learned the following ..."

When an ally takes on the role of the Amplifier, they work to ensure that marginalized voices are both heard and respected. This type of allyship can take many forms, but it is focused on representation within communication.

Here are some ideas for Amplifiers:

- When someone proposes a good idea, repeat it, and give them credit.
- If someone is interrupted, hand back the conversation to them.
- Create openings for people to speak: "Let's pause and hear from any-one who hasn't yet had a chance to speak."
- Upvote or like comments in online discussion forums.
- Share or comment on social media posts.
- Encourage members of underrepresented groups to present their work at meetings, lead training sessions, or submit articles to organization-wide newsletters.

How will you show up as an Amplifier? Here are some exercises to help you identify actions you can take.

EXERCISE 1:
BOOST CONTRIBUTIONS IN MEETINGS

Talk to a marginalized coworker, and they'll tell you about a time (or two or ten) when they felt frustrated, if not downright dejected, in a meeting. Perhaps they couldn't get a word in, were talked over, or ignored. Perhaps someone claimed credit for an idea they had proposed earlier. Perhaps they felt left out of the pre-meeting chatter about a sport or cultural event unfamiliar to them.

In many organizations, meeting culture can be almost comically biased.

To address bias, Amplifiers can act as boosters for inclusion in the meetings they attend, whether in-person or virtual.

Identify a meeting you attend regularly, such as a daily standup, weekly project update, or monthly committee check-in. Write it here.

....

....

....

....

....

....

....

....

Check one or more of the following pledges you commit to taking at the next meeting:

- ☐ I'll pay attention to interruptions and speak up with "Let's let Alex finish their thought" or something similar.
- ☐ I'll endorse points made by people who are members of under-represented groups: "100% agree with what Prithya just said." (This can be done easily via chat in a virtual meeting or out loud for more impact.)
- ☐ I'll look for ideas that get repeated or hijacked and make sure the originator gets credit: "Great idea. Thanks to Jing for surfacing it earlier."
- ☐ I'll recommend creating a shared agenda document where attendees can add comments before or during the meeting (to ensure that everyone can participate in the discussion and get credit for their contributions).
- ☐ I'll create openings for people to speak: "Let's pause and hear from anyone who hasn't yet had a chance to provide their input."
- ☐ If you have another idea to boost contributions write it here.

....

....

....

....

....

To remind yourself to boost contributions in meetings on an ongoing basis, add your pledge to the "Form new habits" page starting on page 91.

EXERCISE 2:
STRENGTHEN YOUR COWORKERS' CREDIBILITY

Coworkers from underrepresented groups can miss out on career-growing opportunities simply because leaders don't know enough about their expertise to consider them. As an Amplifier, encourage people to share their knowledge to build credibility.

Identify how people build credibility and demonstrate competence in your organization. (Check all that apply.)

- ☐ Writing design documents or thought papers

- ☐ Holding lunch-and-learn sessions

- ☐ Giving demonstrations

- ☐ Presenting project updates at meetings

- ☐ Contributing to online discussion forums

- ☐ Publishing articles in internal newsletters

- ☐ Running important meetings

- ☐ Leading task forces

- ☐ Something else: ....

Think about at least one underrepresented coworker whose expertise is not widely known. Write their name here, along with a brief description of the knowledge they have that could be shared more widely:

NAME OF UNDERREPRESENTED COWORKER	THEIR EXPERTISE OR KNOWLEDGE THAT COULD BE MORE VISIBLE AND WIDELY KNOWN

Carefully consider how to encourage them to be more visible. For example, if they've mentioned a career goal to you, point out how sharing their expertise could help them achieve it.

> I was thinking more about your goal to be promoted next year. As you may know, the next level of responsibilities includes leading cross-team initiatives, and I'm not sure enough people know you're already doing this. Are you open to some ideas?

Alternatively, you might explain something you learned from them and ask if they'd be open to sharing it more widely.

> At last week's project update meeting, you shared the approach you took to solving that big problem. Thanks to you, I learned a new technique, and I think others could learn from you, too. Have you considered giving a lunch-and-learn session on it?

The important thing here is not to assume they want to be more visible or need help navigating their career. You're not trying to save them from something terrible or insist you know what's best for them. By contrast, you want to offer to help amplify them, if they'd like the assist.

Be considerate as you think about how to reach out and offer what hopefully will be received as a helpful suggestion. Write down your next steps:

....

....

....

....

....

....

....

....

....

....

....

EXERCISE 3:
AMPLIFY ONLINE VOICES

As Amplifiers, we can use our online presence to share and endorse the voices of marginalized individuals (within our company or our larger community) and professional groups focused on underrepresented talent.

Even if we don't use social media, we can amplify others using our organization's discussion forums, email, and other communication technologies.

Consider an employee resource group (ERG), an external professional association for an underrepresented group, or a few individuals you'd like to amplify. Write their name(s) here.

....

....

....

....

....

....

....

....

....

....

Do you need to learn more about the individuals or groups you'd like to support? Here are some ideas. (Check all that you will do.)

- ☐ Peruse their website
- ☐ Read, watch, or listen to media they've published
- ☐ Subscribe to their mailing list
- ☐ Follow them on social media
- ☐ Something else: ....

Commit to liking or sharing their content on your social media channels or other technology platforms:

- ☐ I'll do this daily
- ☐ I'll do this at least once a week
- ☐ I'll do this at least once a month
- ☐ Another timeframe: ....

If you identified a group to amplify, check out their upcoming events. Jot down one that you will register for and amplify by encouraging coworkers to join you:

EVENT & DATE	I'LL SHARE IT WITH COWORKERS BY

TEAM EXERCISE:
MULTIPLY AMPLIFICATIONS

You can increase your team's impact by amplifying each other's amplifications.

Ask a volunteer or two to share one way they're planning to amplify an individual or group that serves underrepresented colleagues. As a team, discuss how you can further amplify their actions.

For example, if someone is planning to share information on social media about a nonprofit that serves a marginalized demographic, others in the group can offer to like or comment on their post.

Jot down a few ways you will amplify the actions of your team:

....

....

....

....

....

....

....

....

....

....

The Advocate

Shortly after becoming YouTube's CEO, Susan Wojcicki spoke up about how the tech industry titan Bill Campbell had been an ally for her. In an article for *Vanity Fair*, she wrote:

> I learned about an important invitation-only conference convening most of the top leaders in tech and media, yet my name was left off the guest list. Many of the invitees were my peers, meaning that YouTube wouldn't be represented while deals were cut and plans were made. I started to question whether I even belonged at the conference. But rather than let it go, I turned to Bill, someone I knew had a lot of influence and could help fix the situation. He immediately recognized I had a rightful place at the event and within a day he worked his magic and I received my invitation.[8]

In other words, Campbell acted as her Advocate.

Here's one more way an Advocate might take action. A study of nearly 40 million surgical referrals found that male physicians had a strong preference for referring their patients to male surgeons.[9] Over time, this biased tendency disadvantages surgeons of other genders, leading to lower volumes of referrals and contributing to pay disparity. It also may impact patient outcomes, as at least one study found: Women treated by women surgeons were 15 percent less likely than those treated by male surgeons to have complications, readmission to the hospital, or death.[10] I can only hope there are male physicians out there disrupting this norm and ensuring that they are referring patients to women and nonbinary surgeons.

When an ally takes on the role of the Advocate, they use their power and influence to bring coworkers from underrepresented groups into highly exclusive (and often elusive) circles. They advocate for change so everyone can do their best work and thrive.

Here are some specific ways to act as an Advocate:

- Look closely at the invite list for events, strategic planning meetings, dinners with key partners, and other career-building opportunities. If you see someone from an underrepresented group missing, recommend they be invited.
- Ask someone from an underrepresented group to collaborate with you on a project, talk, or conference submission.
- Offer to introduce colleagues from underrepresented groups to influential people in your network.
- Ensure that coworkers from underrepresented groups aren't saddled with undervalued busywork that keeps them from contributing to highly valued initiatives. (More on this in Exercise 1 below.)
- If you're in a position to refer clients to vendors or patients to specialists, make sure that your recommendation list is diverse.

Next up? Some exercises to help you surface your inner Advocate.

EXERCISE 1:
DISRUPT GLUE WORK

Every workplace has glue work that needs to be done for the health of a workgroup but isn't anyone's actual job. (It is also referred to as office housework, undervalued tasks, and non-promotable work.) Examples include scheduling a meeting and taking notes, ordering food, deep-cleaning a shared fridge or lab space, collecting money for a teammate's baby shower, serving on a thankless committee, and organizing a team-building event or DEI initiative. The list goes on (and on).

Women, especially women of color, are tapped for these often unrewarded and undervalued responsibilities more than their white male counterparts. As a result, they're put in subservient roles to their peers, saddled with tasks that take time away from delivering on their primary responsibilities.

In the left column, write down some examples of undervalued but necessary tasks in your workplace that aren't part of someone's job description. Then, in the right column, note how you might advocate for change, either by disrupting the status quo or rewarding someone for taking it on. Here are some suggestions:

- Set up rotation schedules for ongoing tasks so everyone on the team takes a turn.
- Recommend that someone who hasn't done a task before take it on (instead of relying on the person who did a great job with it before or the only person to volunteer).
- Offer to do it yourself (assuming you don't usually raise your hand or get asked to do it).
- Coach a frequent volunteer that taking on these tasks may not help with career growth.

- Advocate for bonus pay or extra paid time off for taking on the task.
- Provide them with administrative support to help get the task done.
- Reward them with a highly sought-after perk. (E.g., specialized training, attending a conference, shadowing an executive, employee-of-the-month parking, etc.)
- Sing their praises and sponsor them for a career-growing opportunity.

UNDERVALUED BUT NECESSARY TASKS THAT AREN'T SOMEONE'S JOB	I CAN DISRUPT WHO USUALLY DOES THESE TASKS OR REWARD THEM FOR DOING SO BY

EXERCISE 2:
SHARE YOUR EXCLUSIVE CIRCLES

Consider your workplace activities, professional circles, and opportunities you might take for granted, yet are elusive to others. For example, being a member of a strategic planning committee, having regular skip-level meetings with a senior leader, playing poker with a group of managers, being consulted for your subject matter expertise, and so on.

Think about one or more professional benefits you receive from being in these situations. Write them here.

....

....

....

....

....

How can you share these exclusive circles or opportunities with a coworker who is a member of an underrepresented group?

....

....

....

....

EXERCISE 3:
ADVOCATE FOR SYSTEMIC CHANGE

While I'm all for simple, everyday actions allies can take to be more inclusive, we also need to consider how to advocate for more meaningful change.

Let's consider the difference between a knight who rides in to save someone in distress and a true ally. It comes down to two things: mindset and systemic change. Allies take action to *empower* individuals rather than rescue them. Allies also seek to create systemic changes instead of making one-off savior moves.

Imagine being on an interview team and hearing biased comments about the only BIPOC candidate. Acting as a knight, you might offer to personally mentor them once they've joined the team to set them up for success.

While this might result in a positive outcome for that one person, better would be to *also* advocate for a change in the hiring process.

> Folks, I'll personally mentor the candidate if we hire them, but let's step back. I'm concerned we're not consistently evaluating candidates. Let's identify objective criteria that we can use to measure everyone. Moving forward, I'd like to discuss how we can make this a best practice for all hiring committees.

As you can see, knight actions aren't inherently bad — but they are often stopgap measures. They may address inequality or discrimination for a single person or group but miss the opportunity to push for long-term change.

Consider something you've done to be an ally for a specific underrepresented coworker. As an Advocate, what's one way you can push for systemic change so that more people can benefit?

....

....

....

....

....

....

....

....

....

....

....

....

....

....

....

....

....

....

....

TEAM EXERCISE:
TAP YOUR TEAM'S INSIDER KNOWLEDGE

As you explored pushing for system change in Exercise 3, you may have come across some roadblocks. Maybe you don't know who is responsible for a process that could be improved. Or you're not sure how to best appeal to a decision maker and influence them to support a change.

Discuss any roadblocks with your team, and brainstorm on ways to help each other. Someone may just have the insider knowledge you need to move forward.

Write some next steps here.

....

....

....

....

....

....

....

....

....

....

The Scholar

I'm a member of the Women's Club of Silicon Valley, a nonprofit leadership incubator for women. Many of our events are open to guests who come to hear the speakers and participate in our workshops. Because most guests are women, it stood out when a man started attending our events. I asked a friend who he was, and she told me he was a former colleague who wanted to better understand the challenges women face in the workplace. He spent many evenings at our events, listening and absorbing information about the issues we discussed so he could be a better ally.

Similarly, I spoke with my college friend Dr. Paul Haut, who most recently worked as the chief operating officer for a large children's hospital in the Midwest. When I asked why inclusion in healthcare workplaces was important to him, he emphasized that providing the best patient care requires respect for people throughout your workplace. Haut admits he had a big awakening soon after George Floyd's murder in May 2020, when he realized, as he put it, "I can't provide equitable care to the patients unless I'm truly living that as an organization with our own teammates. Because if they don't feel respected, how are they going to translate respect to the ones they're caring for?"

Haut then embarked on a journey to learn about addressing racism in the workplace. "It was an intentional, intensive dive into trying to understand and educate myself to even begin to know how to act differently." He added, "This wasn't like continuing education where I was earning credits to maintain a certification; I needed to rethink my whole construct."

When an ally takes on the role of the Scholar, they seek to learn as much as possible about the challenges and prejudices faced by colleagues from marginalized groups. It's important to note that Scholars never insert their own opinions, experiences, or ideas, but instead simply listen and learn. They also don't expect marginalized people to provide links to research proving that bias exists or summaries of best practices. Scholars do their own research to seek out relevant information.

Here are some ideas for acting as a Scholar:

- Read, watch, or listen to books, articles, movies, podcasts, or social media by and about underrepresented groups within your field.
- Attend an event where diversity and inclusion will be the topic of discussion. Listen and learn.
- If your employer or professional association has resource groups or online discussion forums for members of underrepresented groups, ask if you can join to observe. Asking is essential: Your presence may cause members to censor themselves, so be sure to check in before showing up.
- Pay attention to shifts in everyday words and phrases, evolving your language to be more inclusive.
- Share what you learn with colleagues.
- Embrace a growth mindset of continual learning.

Now for some exercises to help you identify how you can be a better Scholar.

EXERCISE 1:
SEEK COMMON GROUND AND EDUCATE

Think of a personal story or anecdote where you learned something about the experience of an underrepresented person or group that surprised you. Or a time you realized that a word or phrase you thought was perfectly fine to use is offensive or demeaning to others.

Then, imagine bringing someone else along on your learning journey with the "Seek common ground and educate approach." It's one of my favorite techniques for better allies, providing a powerful way to speak up about someone's behavior without shaming or blaming them.

Here are some examples of what it might look like:

- "I used to think 'articulate' was a compliment, but I've since learned that many Black people don't view it that way because of the underlying assumption that they couldn't possibly be well-spoken, educated, or highly knowledgeable of a subject area."
- "I used to think it was fine to require a college degree in our job descriptions, but I've since realized that many of the skills we need can be learned on the job and that college is out of reach for many people from lower-income backgrounds."
- "I used to believe that if you worked hard, leaders would notice, and you'd get ahead. But I've seen over and over again that what you really need is a sponsor who will talk about your work and sing your praises."
- "I love scheduling fun, after-work activities for my team, but I'm now more mindful that not everyone has disposable income they can spend on these things. And that some people have caregiving responsibilities outside of work hours. So, I now plan some free and fun things to do during the workday, too."

- "I used to ask student intern candidates about their extracurricular activities, but I've since learned that many students from lower socioeconomic homes have to prioritize after-school jobs over sports and clubs."

Write your anecdote here:

....

....

....

....

....

....

....

....

....

....

....

....

....

....

Now pause and imagine a setting where you can share your story to help others be more inclusive.

EXERCISE 2:
SHARE YOUR KNOWLEDGE

A clever person once said, "Knowledge shared is knowledge squared."

While walking around my neighborhood, I frequently pass by Little Free Libraries. These tiny sheds offer free book exchanges under the motto "Take a book. Share a book." Maybe you've seen them in your community, too.

As a Scholar, chances are you've amassed a nice collection of diversity and inclusion-related books. If that sounds like you, consider creating a tiny library in your office where coworkers can borrow books and add some from their own collection. Take over a shelf in the kitchen, or procure an actual Little Free Library mini-shed to put in a lounge. Then add some books, and see what happens.

Of course, there are many other ways to be generous with sharing what you've learned. I've heard from people who write a monthly column for their employee newsletter or regularly post ideas for being better allies online. Another person told me they host viewing parties to watch talks exploring issues women face in male-dominated workplaces.

Write one thing you already do, or will commit to doing, to share your knowledge about being a better ally:

....

....

....

....

The Better Allies® Way

EXERCISE 3:
EXPAND YOUR LEARNING

As a Scholar, you clearly have a growth mindset, and there's always more to learn.

Reflect on the various identities you've studied. Perhaps you've gravitated to articles and other learning materials about women or Black people in the workplace. Maybe you've focused on understanding the accessibility needs of people with disabilities. If so, you may be less familiar with the experiences and needs of people from other underrepresented groups (e.g., LGBTQ+, older or younger workers, members of a religious group that's not dominant in your area of the world, caregivers, armed services veterans, etc.).

Make a note of a few identities you haven't yet learned about, along with an idea or two of how you can know more about their experiences in the workplace.

TO LEARN MORE ABOUT THIS UNDER-REPRESENTED IDENTITY	I WILL READ ____, WATCH ____, SEARCH ONLINE FOR ____, ATTEND AN ERG MEETING, ETC.

TEAM EXERCISE: LEARN TOGETHER

If you identified an anecdote in Exercise 1 above, share it with the team and pay attention to their reactions. Ask if anyone held a similar misconception or was surprised by your story. Encourage them to elaborate by asking "Tell me more."

As you listen to others' anecdotes, write down things you learned about the experience of an underrepresented person or group.

....

....

....

....

....

....

....

....

....

....

....

The Confidant

I remember chatting with Emily, a college-aged intern who told me about a one-on-one meeting with her mentor. When he asked what she wanted to do post-graduation, Emily emphasized that her top priority was to find an inclusive work environment. When he asked why, she shared her experience working at a previous internship. Her manager there directed all technical questions about her project to her coding partner, a male intern.

The mentor listened to Emily, incredulous at first but then quickly supportive. Although he had heard rumors, he hadn't truly believed things like this happened until she shared this experience with him. By listening and believing, he supported his mentee *and* validated her experience.

While listening, the Confidant might also learn how an individual's experiences impact *how* they do their job.

I spoke to the chief of an emergency department (ED), who I'll refer to as Dr. Jones. Frequently, Jones would hear from medical specialists that they were being consulted too frequently. For example, after being called at 3 a.m. for input on a fracture, an orthopedist might complain to Jones that the ED doctor on duty should have been able to handle it on their own. Receiving and monitoring these issues was simply part of the job.

However, at one point, Jones told me he started receiving a disproportionate number of complaints about one Black ED doctor asking for input from specialists. So he sat down with this doctor to ask about his threshold for calling a consult and his comfort level with managing patient needs himself.

Jones was surprised by the Black doctor's response, who said he felt he needed to consult more often because he was Black. After all, if he were to make a mistake or a wrong decision without consulting, he would be subject to more criticism because of his race.

At that point, a light came on for Jones. He got some insight into this doctor's experience growing up, going through the educational system and medical training, constantly feeling like he needed to perform at a higher level or make fewer mistakes. Because of his race, he chose that practice style. Jones, who is white, would never have known or been able to support him if he hadn't taken the time to talk to him.

When an ally takes on the role of the Confidant, that ally creates a safe space for members of underrepresented groups to express their fears, frustrations, and needs. Simply listening to their stories and trusting that they're being truthful creates a protective layer of support.

Of course, the Confidant shouldn't allow issues to fester and grow. The Confidant believes others when they share their experiences *and* takes action to address the situation (perhaps by donning one of the other seven ally roles).

Some specific ways to act as a Confidant:

- Believe others' experiences. Don't assume something couldn't happen just because you haven't personally experienced it.
- Listen and ask questions when someone describes an experience you haven't had. Don't jump in with your personal stories.
- If you are a supervisor, hold regular "office hours" and encourage your team members to speak with you about issues troubling them.
- Determine how to address the noninclusive behavior you hear about.

EXERCISE 1:
ACKNOWLEDGE OTHERS' EXPERIENCES

Imagine a coworker tells you about a microaggression they just experienced. It could be that they weren't invited to a meeting or included on an email thread. Or they didn't receive credit for their contributions to a project. Or they were interrupted once again in a team meeting.

What would you say? Write your top-of-mind response here:

....

....

....

....

....

....

....

....

....

....

....

....

Now it's time for self-evaluation. If you responded with some form of "I'm sure they didn't intend to exclude you" or "they're like that with everyone," you basically discounted your coworker's experiences and feelings.

A more supportive reply would be, "That's not right. How can I help address what happened?" or "I get it. What are we going to do about it?"

Try writing a supportive response in your own words:

....

....

....

....

....

....

....

....

....

....

....

....

....

....

....

EXERCISE 2:
SEEK FEEDBACK

Here's a paradox that allies need to understand.

If we're part of a dominant group at work, we have some amount of privilege and power. As a result, we may seem less trustworthy to members of marginalized groups. Without trust, people are less likely to want our support as allies. Furthermore, we're less likely to receive feedback from the groups we aim to support, leading us to believe that everything we do is helpful and effective.[11]

In other words, our power can get in the way of being a competent ally.

As Confidants, we can and should seek feedback so that a) more people trust us and b) we learn how to support them best. For example, "How did you feel about my approach to including your voice in the discussion? Any suggestions for next time?"

Or, ask a coworker from an underrepresented demographic, "What's one thing I could be doing differently to better support you or create a more inclusive workplace?"

Identify something you've recently done to be more inclusive. Write it here, along with an idea or two of how you can seek feedback on the action you took:

....

....

....

The Better Allies® Way

EXERCISE 3:
BE CURIOUS, NOT FURIOUS

As a Confidant, you may get feedback that you are (or a group you belong to is) doing something noninclusive. It's never fun, but without constructive feedback, we can never improve.

Upon receiving feedback, you may get defensive. (I certainly do.) One approach I find incredibly helpful is to **be curious, not furious**. It's a perfect mindset for those times when someone disagrees with us or points out when we've made a mistake on the journey to being a better ally.

Reflect on a recent time you got constructive feedback. (Ideally, about something you could have done to be a better ally, but any example will do.) Describe what it was about:

....

....

....

....

....

....

....

....

How did you feel when you received it? (Check all that apply.)

☐ Defensive   ☐ Empathetic
☐ Embarrassed   ☐ Thankful
☐ In denial   ☐ Inspired
☐ Incredulous   ☐ Curious
☐ Angry   ☐ Something else
☐ Ambivalent

....

If you checked one or more feelings on the left side, what question(s) could you have asked to help you be curious and learn more about the feedback?

....

....

....

....

....

....

....

....

....

....

TEAM EXERCISE:
ELEVATE EXISTING FEEDBACK CHANNELS

Let's face it: There's strength in numbers. If you're doing this workbook with others, you can increase your impact as a Confidant by identifying how your overall organization can better collect (and act on) feedback to be more inclusive.

Consider how employees in your organization provide feedback today. For example,

- 360° performance reviews

- One-on-one meetings

- Project retrospectives

- Internal surveys

- Anonymous suggestion boxes

Other ways

- ....

- ....

- ....

- ....

Discuss how you can leverage these approaches to get feedback on how your organization can be more inclusive. Write a few ideas and next steps here:

....

....

....

....

....

....

....

....

....

....

....

....

....

....

....

....

....

....

The Upstander

Now for the most challenging ally role for many of us: the Upstander.

The Upstander sees wrongdoing and acts to combat it. They push back on offensive comments or jokes, even if no one within earshot might be offended or hurt. They are the opposite of a bystander — someone who does nothing, perhaps because they don't know what to do or say, are frozen with fear, or simply don't care.

Why might it be challenging to be an Upstander? As Brené Brown, PhD, noted in her book *Dare to Lead*,

> People are opting out of vital conversations about diversity and inclusivity because they fear looking wrong, saying something wrong, or being wrong. Choosing our own comfort over hard conversations is the epitome of privilege, and it corrodes trust and moves us away from meaningful and lasting change.[12]

But here's the thing. The world needs more Upstanders, especially with the growing concern about the treatment of Black people in many countries, the increase in legislation limiting LGBTQ+ rights, the rise in incidents of anti-Semitism, and other hate crimes against ethnic minorities, to name just some of the disturbing trends.

We need more people who observe wrongdoing and take action. People who push for change. People who aren't comfortable with the status quo, even though they may have benefited from it.

The stories of Upstanders inspire me. For example, I remember hearing from Lisa, a white software engineer who stepped outside her comfort zone to be an ally. When asked to name her "spirit animal" as part of a team-building exercise, Lisa spoke up. She explained that she wasn't comfortable participating in an activity that appropriated Native American spiritual traditions.

Then there's Erika, a newsletter subscriber who attended a music performance where the conductor used both ableist and sexist language in response to a soloist's dress. Looking at her, he said, "I'm old, not blind," and hundreds of audience members laughed. Afterward, Erika provided feedback through a survey that these off-the-cuff "jokes" were not okay. She told me, "It's the smallest thing I can do, but it is an action item."

Another newsletter subscriber, Mark, told me about a recent meeting where a leader used the phrase "this document serves several masters." They then listed the positions of the people who would use the document. Mark told me, "At first, I was shocked." He added, "I knew I had to say something, but I wondered if I should do it in the meeting or privately?"

I bet many of us have been in the same situation. I know I have. Should we speak up in the moment or wait to provide feedback in private?

Mark decided to say something right then and there, even though he admitted, "It was truly uncomfortable to call out a manager two levels up."

When the leader asked if there were any questions, Mark replied, "Speaking as an ally, could I ask you to please use a different phrase instead of 'serves several masters' and go with 'serves several purposes'?"

The leader looked a little surprised. But he repeated the phrase Mark suggested and said that he could use that in the future.

Mark also told me, "Being an ally is not always easy, but it is necessary to show it."

Here are some ways to act as an Upstander:

- Always speak up if you witness behavior or speech that is noninclusive, degrading, or offensive. Explain your stance so everyone knows why you are raising the issue.
- During meetings, shut down off-topic questions that are asked only to test the person speaking.
- Take action if you see anyone being bullied or harassed. Simply insert yourself into a conversation with a comment like "Hi! What are you folks discussing?" and then check in with the victim privately. Ask if they are okay and if they want you to say something to the harassers or a supervisor.

Even if being an Upstander means taking a giant step outside of your comfort zone, I urge you to do so. And I have some exercises to help.

EXERCISE 1:
UNDERSTAND WHAT HOLDS YOU BACK

Think of a time you witnessed discrimination, bias, or noninclusive behavior or language and didn't know what to do or say. Describe it here:

....

....

....

....

....

....

....

....

....

....

....

....

....

....

Why didn't you speak up or take action? (Check all that apply.)

- ☐ I couldn't find the right words to use
- ☐ I didn't want to call someone out or embarrass them
- ☐ I was concerned I might cause more harm than good
- ☐ I was worried about what others might think of me for speaking up
- ☐ I was concerned about my personal safety
- ☐ It happened so fast; I didn't realize what was happening until later
- ☐ Something else ....

The following exercises will help you identify how to act in many situations.

EXERCISE 2:
CREATE CONVERSATIONAL SPEED BUMPS

One approach we can use when hearing a disparaging or biased comment or joke is slowing down the conversation with the equivalent of a conversational speed bump.

Here are some suggestions from the "Dear Ally Skills Trainer" advice column:[13]

- "I didn't quite catch that, but here are my thoughts on what we were discussing..."
- "Sorry, my sound dropped out for a second there, but the gist of what you are saying is [repeat without the oppressive comment], right?"
- "I'm afraid I don't get the joke. Let's move on..."
- "I think I've lost the thread of the conversation. What about [topic]?"

By slowing things down, we can start back up on a more inclusive footing. We also give the person who commented or joked a chance to reflect on what they said without being called out.

While we can use speed bumps in many situations, they're especially helpful if the balance of power is not in our favor. For example, when the person who made the comment is a client, someone more senior, or an intimidating peer.

Reflect on the situation you noted above in Exercise 1. Could you have used a speed bump to redirect the conversation in a more inclusive way? What would you say?

EXERCISE 3:
IDENTIFY YOUR GO-TO PHRASE

While speed bumps are good for quickly redirecting a conversation in a more inclusive way, there are times we should pause and speak out against biased, offensive, or inappropriate behavior.

Does coming forward and objecting feel uncomfortable? For many of us, the answer is a resounding "Heck yes." But this discomfort is nothing compared to how it feels for the person whose racial group is being joked about. Or the colleague who is forced to endure constant commentary about her appearance. Or the coworker who is being excluded due to a disability. The discomfort of allies pales compared to what people from marginalized groups are forced to live through daily for the entire duration of their lives.

To be prepared, having some scripted responses in your back pocket is helpful. In the moment, you might freeze up and doubt yourself, so memorize a few stock callouts so you're ready to confront inappropriate jokes and comments. Here are a few suggestions:

- "I don't get it. Can you explain the joke to me?" This forces the speaker to dig into their reasoning aloud, which brings bigotry to light.
- "That wasn't funny."
- "Wow, that was awkward."
- "Did you really just say that?"
- "Ouch."

Another idea is to respond with a simple "We don't do that here."

I learned about the power of this phrase in a blog post by Aja Hammerly, a developer relations manager at Google. She wrote:

The college I attended was small and very LGBT friendly. One day someone came to visit and used the word "gay" as a pejorative. A student looked at the visitor and flatly said, "We don't do that here." The guest started getting defensive and explaining that they weren't homophobic and didn't mean anything by it. The student replied, "I'm sure that's true, but all you need to know is we don't do that here." The interaction ended at that point, and everyone moved on to different topics. "We don't do that here" was a polite but firm way to educate the newcomer about our culture.[14]

Think of yourself as an Upstander who can and does speak up. Visualize yourself seeing injustice and taking action. What will be your go-to phrase?

....

....

....

....

....

....

....

....

....

....

....

....

....

EXERCISE 4:
ASK CLARIFYING QUESTIONS

Imagine you've interviewed a candidate who asked about your Pride employee group. During the debrief meeting, a coworker says they don't think the candidate would fit in with the team. Your spidey sense starts tingling. You might assume that your coworker is homophobic and doesn't want to work with someone who is LGBTQ+.

But what if it's something else? Something not rooted in bias?

Instead of making assumptions, an Upstander can ask open-ended questions with sincere curiosity and respect to clarify what's happening. Not to trick them, but to genuinely be curious. For example, "Tell me more" or "What makes you say that?" or "What makes you feel that way?"

In this scenario, you may learn something about the candidate's skill set or background that you didn't glean from the interview. Or, if your coworker *was* making a biased comment, this approach gets them to confront their thinking, forcing them to dig into their reasoning aloud. They may decide it's not worth explaining and drop the topic quickly.

Think about a time when you assumed someone was biased because of their words or actions. What clarifying questions could you have asked to understand better what was happening?

....

....

....

....

....

....

....

....

....

EXERCISE 5:
WORK UP YOUR COURAGE FOR A REDO

Even with the exercises above, we may miss the opportunity to be an Upstander. Perhaps something happened so fast that we didn't realize it was noninclusive until later. Or maybe we didn't want to disrupt a large meeting. Or we couldn't speak up quickly enough with our go-to phrase. I get it. Regardless of the reason, we can always circle back and revisit the situation.

In her book *The Wake Up: Closing the Gap Between Good Intentions and Real Change*, Michelle MiJung Kim implores us to "work up your courage for a redo."[15]

She shares some suggested phrases we can use to revisit a situation:

- "Hey, can we check in about something that happened last week?"
- "I'm sorry I didn't address this earlier, but I've given it some thought and want to share this."
- "I've not been able to get this off my mind. Can we have a quick chat?"

Reflect on a time when you didn't take action as an Upstander. How could you have brought up your concern or feedback after the fact? Write a few notes about what was going on and your thoughts on how to approach a "redo."

TEAM EXERCISE:
SUPPORT EACH OTHER

As I mentioned earlier, being an Upstander can be the most challenging role on the journey to being a better ally. After all, it takes courage to speak up when witnessing noninclusive or discriminatory behavior, especially if it means stepping outside of your comfort zone.

Consider a scenario where acting as an Upstander might be difficult for you. Describe it here:

....

....

....

....

....

....

....

....

....

....

....

Share the scenario with your group, and ask how others would act if they encountered it. Note anything that would help you be a better Upstander.

....
....
....
....
....
....
....
....
....
....
....
....
....
....
....
....
....
....
....

....

....

....

....

....

....

....

....

....

....

....

....

....

....

....

....

....

....

....

....

What now?

Congratulations! You've made it through all seven archetypes. I'm sure you're excited to get started on the actions you identified in the exercises.

To hold yourself accountable, review the actions you noted in the exercises for each archetype and consider *when* you will do them.

- ☐ Ideally, you'll have the opportunity to do many of them within the next 30 days. Record them on "My 30-day plan" in the next section so they're in one handy place you can refer to daily or weekly.
- ☐ Some actions won't be just "one and done." There will be things that you want to do on an ongoing basis. To ensure that you keep doing them moving forward, you may need to form new habits. Record these in the "Form new habits" page starting on page 91.

As I mentioned earlier, some roles may be more natural for you than others. I encourage you to double down on the ones that feel most like you, since you'll most likely have the biggest impact there.

Which feels most natural to you? (Check all that apply.)

- ☐ Sponsor
- ☐ Champion
- ☐ Amplifier
- ☐ Advocate
- ☐ Scholar
- ☐ Confidant
- ☐ Upstander

For the roles that are "most like you," how can you lean into them further? Write some ideas here:

....

....

....

....

....

....

....

....

....

....

....

....

....

....

....

That said, I hope you've identified actions to take under the roles that aren't as natural for you. As the saying goes, stepping outside of your comfort zone is where the magic happens. By doing so, you'll help create an even more inclusive workplace, where everyone can do their best work and thrive.

Think about how you can build strengths for the role that feels most challenging to you:

The role I find most challenging is:

....

To get better at being this kind of ally, I will:

....

....

....

....

....

....

....

....

One last thing. If you did this workbook with others, consider pairing up with an "accountability buddy" to help ensure that you both shift your behavior to be a better ally.

ACCOUNTABILITY BUDDY

My accountability buddy is:

....

We will check in with each other (circle one of the following):

Weekly   Biweekly   Monthly

We will connect via:

☐   text message

☐   email

☐   video or phone call

☐   in-person chat

☐   Or ....

My 30-day plan

AS A SPONSOR, I WILL

AS A CHAMPION, I WILL

....
....
....
....
....
....
....
....
....
....
....
....
....
....
....
....
....

AS AN AMPLIFIER, I WILL

AS AN ADVOCATE, I WILL

AS A SCHOLAR, I WILL

....

....

....

....

....

....

....

....

....

....

....

....

....

....

....

....

....

....

AS A CONFIDANT, I WILL

....

....

....

....

....

....

....

....

....

....

....

....

....

....

....

....

AS AN UPSTANDER, I WILL

Form new habits

Use the pages in this section to jot down actions you want to take monthly, quarterly, or yearly. By writing them here and referring to these pages regularly, you'll be better set up to take action and help create a more inclusive workplace culture for all.

MONTHLY, I WILL...

....

....

....

....

....

....

....

....

....

....

....

QUARTERLY, I WILL...

YEARLY, I WILL...

Keep learning

I hope you've found this workbook helpful, though it is just one resource. My three other books dive into more detail and provide loads of inspiration and practical everyday actions for how to be a better ally. You can purchase *Better Allies*, *The Better Allies Approach to Hiring*, and *Belonging in Healthcare* from online retailers, request them at your local bookstore, or borrow them from your school or community library.

If you did this work as part of a team, consider forming a book club for one of my books. You'll find discussion guides to help facilitate the conversation at *www.betterallies.com*.

I've also curated a collection of books about how to be more inclusive by other authors. You can view them at *www.bookshop.org/shop/BetterAllies*.

If you prefer newsletters, please subscribe to my free "5 Ally Actions" email. Each week, I share ideas curated from the news and my interactions with subscribers, audience members, and social media followers from around the world. I'm on a mission to be a better ally myself and regularly uncover new approaches. And when I make mistakes, I write about them in the newsletter so others can learn with me. You can view some past editions and subscribe at *www.betterallies.com*.

Or, if social media is your thing, I'd love to have you follow @BetterAllies on Instagram, Medium, Threads, or X. You can also find me, Karen Catlin, on LinkedIn.

What are some resources you'll use to keep learning?

....

....

....

....

....

....

....

....

....

....

Being an ally is a journey, and I'm thrilled you're joining me. I also hope you feel a sense of urgency to take the actions you've identified through the exercises in this workbook and to keep learning.

Personally, I'm inspired by Maya Angelou, who wisely said: "Do the best you can until you know better. Then when you know better, do better."[16]

Together, we can all do better and make a difference in workplaces everywhere.

–Karen Catlin

Notes

The Better Allies® Way

The Better Allies® Way

The Better Allies® Way

Endnotes

1   Colleen Flaherty, "Help That Hurts Women," Inside Higher Ed, June 19, 2018, https://www.insidehighered.com/news/2018/06/19/study-finds-recommendation-letters-inadvertently-signal-doubt-about-female.

2   Hebl et al., "How We Describe Male and Female Job Applicants Differently," September 27, 2018, Harvard Business Review, https://hbr.org/2018/09/how-we-describe-male-and-female-job-applicants-differently.

3   Andrew Grill, "I Gave Up My Seat at an All-Male Panel to a Woman— And More Men Should Do the Same," Huffington Post, May 27, 2015, https://www.huffingtonpost.com/andrew-grill/i-gave-up-my-seat-at-an-all-male-panel-to-a-woman_b_7451512.html.

4   Helen Murphy, "Leaked update to pandemic accord sparks discord at WHA," Devex Newswire, May 26, 2023, https://www-devex-com.cdn.ampproject.org/c/s/www.devex.com/news/devex-newswire-leaked-update-to-pandemic-accord-sparks-discord-at-wha-105589/amp.

5   AnitaB.org, "Megan Smith - Importance of Diverse Ideas in Gov't GHC15," YouTube video, November 30, 2015, 23:19, https://www.youtube.com/watch?v=ILzUpCA_ozE.

6   Claire Landsbaum, "Obama's Female Staffers Came Up with a Genius Strategy to Make Sure Their Voices Were Heard," The Cut, September 13, 2016, https://www.thecut.com/2016/09/heres-how-obamas-female-staffers-made-their-voices-heard.html.

7   "The Power of Allyship," webinar hosted by American Association of Women in Radiology, November 11, 2021, https://www.aawr.org/Events/Webinar-Archives.

8   Susan Wojcicki, "Exclusive: How to Break Up the Silicon Valley Boys' Club," *Vanity Fair*, March 16, 2017, https://www.vanityfair.com/news/2017/03/how-to-break-up-the-silicon-valley-boys-club-susan-wojcicki.

9   Fahima Dossa et al., "Sex Differences in the Pattern of Patient Referrals to Male and Female Surgeons," JAMA Surgery, November 10, 2022;157(2):95–103, https://jamanetwork.com/journals/jamasurgery/article-abstract/2786065.

10 Christopher J. D. Wallis et al., "Association of Surgeon-Patient Sex Concordance With Postoperative Outcomes," JAMA Surgery, December 8, 2021, https://doi.org/10.1001/jamasurg.2021.6339.

11 Karren Knowlton, Andrew M.Carton, and Adam M.Grant, "Help (Un) wanted: Why the most powerful allies are the most likely to stumble — and when they fulfill their potential," https://www.sciencedirect.com/science/article/pii/S0191308522000260.

12 Brené Brown, *Dare to Lead* (New York: Random House, 2018).

13 Valerie Aurora, "What Do I Do About Oppressive Speech From Clients," Dear Ally Skills Trainer Advice Column, accessed May 15, 2019, no longer available online.

14 Aja Hammerly, "We Don't Do That Here," Thagomizer, September 29, 2017, https://thagomizer.com/blog/2017/09/29/we-don-t-do-that-here.html.

15 Michelle MiJung Kim, *The Wake Up: Closing the Gap Between Good Intentions and Real Change* (New York: Hatchett Go, 2021).

16 "Quotable Quote," Goodreads, accessed October 19, 2020, https://www.goodreads.com/quotes/7273813-do-the-best-you-can-until-you-know-better-then.

About the Author

After spending 25 years building software products and serving as a vice president of engineering at Macromedia and Adobe, Karen Catlin witnessed a sharp decline in the number of women working in tech. Frustrated but galvanized, she knew it was time to switch gears.

Today, Karen is a leadership coach and a highly acclaimed author and speaker on inclusive workplaces. She coaches women to be stronger leaders and people of all gender identities to be better allies. Her client roster includes Airbnb, DoorDash, Google, and Intuit, as well as entrepreneurs and individuals. Her writing on leadership topics has appeared in *Inc.*, the *Daily Beast*, *Fast Company*, and *The Muse*, and she's consulted on articles for the *Wall Street Journal*, *Forbes*, and the *New York Times*.

In late 2014, Karen started the Twitter handle @BetterAllies to share simple, actionable steps that anyone could take to make their workplaces more inclusive. That Twitter handle became the inspiration for four books: *Better Allies®*, *The Better Allies® Approach to Hiring*, *Belonging in Healthcare*, and *The Better Allies® Way*. She also emails a roundup of "5 Ally Actions" to over 35,000 newsletter subscribers every week.

A self-professed public speaking geek, Karen is a highly sought-after and engaging presenter who has delivered talks at hundreds of conferences and corporate events. Her TEDx talk, "Women in Tech: The Missing Force," explores the decline in gender diversity in tech, why it's a problem, and what can be done about it. In addition to speaking herself, Karen is determined to change the ratio of who is onstage giving keynotes and other presentations. To support her goal of bringing more diversity to speaker lineups at tech industry events, she co-authored the book *Present! A Techie's Guide to Public Speaking* with engineer and entrepreneur Poornima Vijayashanker.

Karen is a graduate and active alum of Brown University, mentoring women computer science students on how to launch their careers. She's also a member of the board of directors of Digital NEST and on the advisory boards for the Women's Club of Silicon Valley and WEST (Women Entering & Staying in Technology). In 2015, the California State Assembly honored Karen with the Wonder Women Tech Innovator Award for outstanding achievements in business and technology and for being a role model for women.

Karen and her husband, Tim, live in San Mateo, California. They're the proud parents of Emma and Ted.

Learn more at *www.karencatlin.com* and *www.betterallies.com*.

Printed in the USA
CPSIA information can be obtained
at www.ICGtesting.com
LVHW052026240124
769471LV00096B/3816